Carol Vorderman

Maths ✓
Made Easy
ExtraTests

Author and consultant Sean McArdle

Key Stage 2
AGES
9-10

LONDON, NEW YORK, MUNICH, MELBOURNE, and DELHI

DK UK
Senior Editor Deborah Lock
Art Director Martin Wilson
Publishing Director Sophie Mitchell
Pre-production Francesca Wardell
Jacket Designer Martin Wilson
Maths Consultant Sean McArdle

DK Delhi
Editorial Monica Saigal, Tanya Desai
Design Pallavi Narain, Dheeraj Arora,
Tanvi Nathyal, Jyotsna Khosla
DTP Designer Anita Yadav

First published in Great Britain by
Dorling Kindersley Limited
80 Strand, London, WC2R 0RL

Copyright © 2013 Dorling Kindersley Limited
A Penguin Company

10 9 8 7 6 5 4 3 2 1
001—187386—July/2013

A CIP catalogue record for this book
is available from the British Library
ISBN: 978-1-4093-2366-2

Printed and bound in China by L. Rex Printing Co., Ltd.

All images © Dorling Kindersley
For further information see: www.dkimages.com

Discover more at
www.dk.com

Contents

This chart lists all the topics in the book. Once you have completed each page, stick a star in the correct box below.

★ Place value

Write each of these in numbers.

Fifteen thousand, seven hundred and twenty nine | 15 729

Six hundred and eighteen thousand, two hundred and forty three

Five million, six hundred thousand and four

One hundred and seven thousand, two hundred and fifty six

Three hundred thousand, two hundred and eighteen

Eight hundred and six thousand, one hundred and seven

Three hundred and twenty-one thousand, five hundred and fifty nine

Nine hundred and ninety-nine thousand, nine hundred and ninety nine

Two million, three hundred and forty-seven thousand, one hundred and sixty nine

Eight million, two hundred and five thousand, four hundred and one

Write each row in order, starting with the smallest number.

721 358	8 213 560	6 234 078	1 200 000

9 999 999	999 999	10 000 000	9 000 009

Write each number in words.

2 301 502 ....

7 582 416 ....

Write the answers.

269 x 10 = 2 690

845 x 10 =

1 564 x 10 =

7 405 x 10 =

7 420 x 10 =

15 645 x 10 =

23 785 x 10 =

54 866 x 10 =

299 400 x 10 =

324 545 x 10 =

465 212 x 10 =

2 867 x 100 =

26 734 x 100 =

65 089 x 100 =

72 967 x 100 =

300 000 x 100 =

7 650 ÷ 10 =

52 430 ÷ 10 =

76 400 ÷ 10 =

600 000 ÷ 10 =

1 435 290 ÷ 10 =

1 350 000 ÷ 10 =

5 500 430 ÷ 10 =

8 412 600 ÷ 10 =

10 000 000 ÷ 10 =

376 800 ÷ 100 =

656 000 ÷ 100 =

1 345 000 ÷ 100 =

5 000 000 ÷ 100 =

5 560 200 ÷ 100 =

8 400 000 ÷ 100 =

8 006 000 ÷ 100 =

Write each row in order, starting with the smallest number.

7 m	690 cm	1.6 km	900 m	1 700 m
690 cm				

23 cm	240 mm	180 mm	20 cm	0.21 m

2.8 km	3 000 m	2.5 km	2 600 m	1.9 km

678 g	0.5 kg	2.3 kg	1 400 g	0.95 kg

1 200 ml	1.6 l	0.9 l	850 ml	1 400 ml

£5.50	280 p	£0.75	600 p	£3.90

12 l	11 000 ml	8.5 l	110.45 ml	6.85 l

150 seconds	3 minutes	1 hour	130 minutes	600 seconds

$\frac{1}{2}$ l	$\frac{3}{5}$ l	1.2 l	0.25 l	2 l

2 hours	50 minutes	$3\frac{1}{2}$ hours	100 minutes	$1\frac{1}{2}$ hours

Constant steps ★

Continue each sequence.

1.6	2.2	2.8	3.4	4.0	4.6		
3.7	4.2	4.7	5.2	5.7			
$1\frac{1}{2}$	$4\frac{1}{2}$	$7\frac{1}{2}$	$10\frac{1}{2}$	$13\frac{1}{2}$			
35	28	21	14	7			
5.9	4.9	3.9	2.9	1.9			
$6\frac{1}{4}$	$5\frac{3}{4}$	$5\frac{1}{4}$	$4\frac{3}{4}$	$4\frac{1}{4}$			
−6.5	−5.6	−4.7	−3.8	−2.9			
34	45	56	67	78			
8.6	9.2	9.8	10.4	11.0			
30	45	60	75	90			
−50	−44	−38	−32	−26			
0.6	1.1	1.6	2.1	2.6			
4.6	7.6	10.6	13.6	16.6			
14.4	13.9	13.4	12.9	12.4			
7.3	6.3	5.3	4.3	3.3			

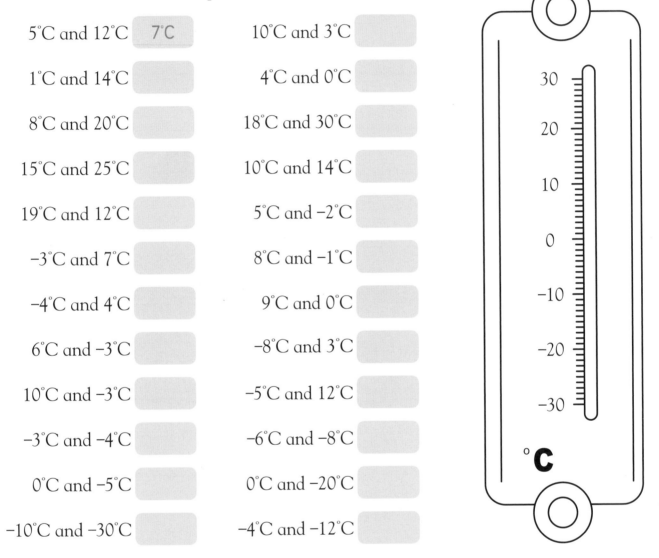

★ Calculating temperatures

Use the thermometer to count the number of degrees from one temperature to another to answer these questions.

What is the difference in temperatures?

5°C and 12°C **7°C**   10°C and 3°C

1°C and 14°C   4°C and 0°C

8°C and 20°C   18°C and 30°C

15°C and 25°C   10°C and 14°C

19°C and 12°C   5°C and −2°C

−3°C and 7°C   8°C and −1°C

−4°C and 4°C   9°C and 0°C

6°C and −3°C   −8°C and 3°C

10°C and −3°C   −5°C and 12°C

−3°C and −4°C   −6°C and −8°C

0°C and −5°C   0°C and −20°C

−10°C and −30°C   −4°C and −12°C

The temperature in London, U.K. is 5°C but the temperature in Moscow, Russia is 8°C colder. What is the temperature in Moscow?

The temperature in Madrid, Spain is 12°C warmer than the temperature in Toronto, Canada. The temperature in Toronto is −3°C. What is the temperature in Madrid?

The temperature in Paris, France is 7°C and in Helsinki, Finland is −4°C. What is the difference in temperature between Paris and Helsinki?

Fractions of amounts ⭐

What is one-quarter ($\frac{1}{4}$) of each amount?

12 p `3 p`   40 p   60 p   £1.00   £8.00

24 cm   36 cm   4 m   16 cm   240 cm

8 kg   28 g   44 kg   52 kg   120 g

What is two-thirds ($\frac{2}{3}$) of each amount?

21 km   27 kg   15 p   £30   18 cm

12 l   9 cm   30 m   45 kg   60 mm

24 ml   36 m   90 km   48 cm   £120

What is three-quarters ($\frac{3}{4}$) of each amount?

£1.00   £1.60   £1.12   £1.40   £10.00

96 p   84 p   72 p   56 p   104 p

240 m   400 m   600 m   480 m   220 m

What is four-fifths ($\frac{4}{5}$) of each amount?

350 g   8 m   £5   15 km   20 m

100 mm   80 m   60 p   90 cm   30 p

500 km   £2   250 p   £120   900 m

Write each fraction in its decimal form.

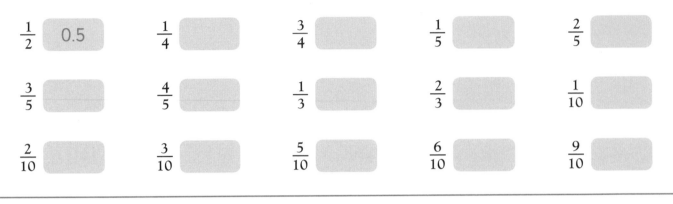

$\frac{1}{2}$ [0.5] $\frac{1}{4}$ [ ] $\frac{3}{4}$ [ ] $\frac{1}{5}$ [ ] $\frac{2}{5}$ [ ]

$\frac{3}{5}$ [ ] $\frac{4}{5}$ [ ] $\frac{1}{3}$ [ ] $\frac{2}{3}$ [ ] $\frac{1}{10}$ [ ]

$\frac{2}{10}$ [ ] $\frac{3}{10}$ [ ] $\frac{5}{10}$ [ ] $\frac{6}{10}$ [ ] $\frac{9}{10}$ [ ]

Write each number in its decimal form.

$1\frac{1}{2}$ [1.5] $7\frac{1}{2}$ [ ] $4\frac{1}{3}$ [ ] $7\frac{2}{3}$ [ ] $9\frac{1}{4}$ [ ]

$6\frac{1}{5}$ [ ] $9\frac{3}{10}$ [ ] $2\frac{9}{10}$ [ ] $12\frac{1}{3}$ [ ] $15\frac{2}{3}$ [ ]

$8\frac{4}{5}$ [ ] $5\frac{3}{4}$ [ ] $7\frac{8}{10}$ [ ] $15\frac{3}{5}$ [ ] $2\frac{4}{10}$ [ ]

$14\frac{2}{3}$ [ ] $18\frac{3}{4}$ [ ] $12\frac{3}{4}$ [ ] $2\frac{1}{2}$ [ ] $15\frac{6}{10}$ [ ]

Join the shaded fraction to its decimal form with a line.

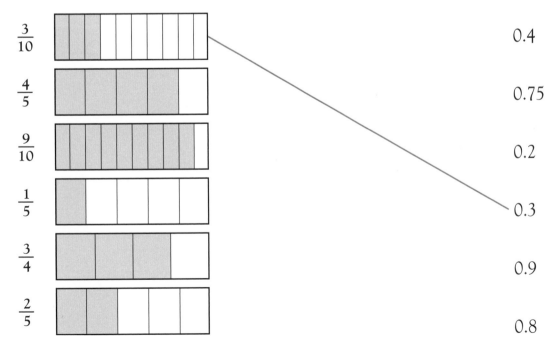

$\frac{3}{10}$ 0.4

$\frac{4}{5}$ 0.75

$\frac{9}{10}$ 0.2

$\frac{1}{5}$ 0.3

$\frac{3}{4}$ 0.9

$\frac{2}{5}$ 0.8

Change each fraction to its percentage equivalent.

$\frac{1}{2}$ = 50% $\frac{1}{4}$ = $\frac{3}{4}$ = $\frac{1}{5}$ =

$\frac{2}{5}$ = $\frac{3}{5}$ = $\frac{4}{5}$ = $\frac{1}{10}$ =

$\frac{2}{10}$ = $\frac{3}{10}$ = $\frac{4}{10}$ = $\frac{5}{10}$ =

$\frac{6}{10}$ = $\frac{7}{10}$ = $\frac{8}{10}$ = $\frac{9}{10}$ =

$\frac{50}{100}$ = $\frac{80}{100}$ = $\frac{10}{100}$ = $\frac{20}{100}$ =

$\frac{90}{100}$ = $\frac{40}{100}$ = $\frac{70}{100}$ = $\frac{30}{100}$ =

$\frac{60}{100}$ = $\frac{25}{100}$ = $\frac{75}{100}$ = $\frac{5}{100}$ =

$\frac{17}{100}$ = $\frac{28}{100}$ = $\frac{35}{100}$ = $\frac{46}{100}$ =

$\frac{52}{100}$ = $\frac{63}{100}$ = $\frac{76}{100}$ = $\frac{83}{100}$ =

Write each amount as a percentage of one pound (£).

27 p 27%   35 p   60 p   90 p

41 p   12 p   42 p   79 p

75 p   56 p   30 p   80 p

What is 20% of each amount? **Hint:** 20% = $\frac{20}{100}$ or $\frac{1}{5}$.

£2.00   £5.00   10 km   400 m

Ten people win a lottery prize of £1 345 279. The prize is shared equally between them. How much will they each receive?

A scientist has to put some animals on display in order of their length. The smallest animal must go first. Below are the lengths of some animals. Put these lengths in order, starting with the shortest.

27 m	3 750 cm	18.25 m	99 mm	0.87 m

A child reduces each of these amounts by 8 units every minute. What will the amounts be after 5 minutes?

	After 1 min	After 2 min	After 3 min	After 4 min	After 5 min
62 g					
79 cm					
102 ml					

The temperature in a freezer drops steadily by 2°C per hour. If the freezer starts at −1°C, what will the temperature be after six hours?

Put each row in order, starting with the smallest number.

7.5	5.7	7.05	5.07	5.55	5.75
12.8	1.28	0.12	0.28	2.18	1.82
34.06	30.46	36.4	36.04	30.64	34.6

Circle the fractions that are equivalent to $\frac{3}{4}$.

$\frac{30}{40}$ $\frac{9}{10}$ $\frac{4}{6}$ $\frac{12}{16}$ $\frac{300}{400}$ $\frac{18}{30}$

Boris has five children. Each child has a certain amount of money.

Annie £12.00   Billy £20.00   Carol £18.00   Doris £24.00   David £8.00

Boris tells each child they must give one-fifth of their money to charity. How much will each child give?

Annie	Billy	Carol	Doris	David

Write the answers.

$\frac{4}{5}$ of £14 = $\frac{3}{4}$ of 80 cm = $\frac{3}{10}$ of 2 m =

$\frac{2}{5}$ of 4 m = $\frac{2}{3}$ of 60 km = $\frac{9}{10}$ of 800 g =

Circle the fractions that are equivalent to 0.4.

$\frac{3}{4}$ $\frac{2}{5}$ $\frac{1}{2}$ $\frac{1}{3}$ $\frac{4}{10}$ $\frac{4}{8}$

What is 30% of each amount? **Hint:** 30% = $\frac{30}{100}$ or $\frac{3}{10}$.

£8   2 m   150 cm

£20   60 g   £100

13

Circle the multiples of 12.

| 50 | (24) | 60 | 144 |

| 38 | 70 | 80 | 100 | 90 |

| 36 | 120 | 56 | 94 |

Circle the multiples of 15.

| 45 | 10 | 60 | 130 |

| 80 | 70 | 75 | 100 | 90 |

| 1 | 150 | 50 | 65 |

Circle the multiples of 20.

| 15 | 20 | 310 | 110 |

| 60 | 90 | 70 | 100 | 400 |

| 500 | 130 | 200 | 30 |

Circle the multiples of 50.

| 50 | 20 | 350 | 500 |

| 750 | 1 000 | 70 | 100 | 400 |

| 300 | 130 | 240 | 470 |

Write the factors of these numbers. Always begin with 1.
Remember: If a number is even, 2 will always be a factor.

The factors of 10 are | 1, 2, 5, 10

The factors of 12 are |

The factors of 18 are |

The factors of 51 are |

The factors of 61 are |

The factors of 71 are |

The factors of 81 are |

The factors of 60 are |

The factors of 70 are |

The factors of 75 are |

The factors of 85 are |

The factors of 29 are |

The factors of 53 are |

The factors of 24 are |

Work out these multiplication sums, using the method you prefer.

48 x 11	67 x 12	79 x 13	54 x 14

```
    48
x   11
_____
    48
+  480
_____
   528
```

23 x 15	85 x 16	35 x 17	46 x 18

59 x 19	123 x 21	68 x 23	154 x 25

143 x 27	135 x 13	214 x 15	167 x 16

Dividing with remainders ★

You may have been shown different ways to work out these problems.
Use the method you prefer to find the quotient and remainders.

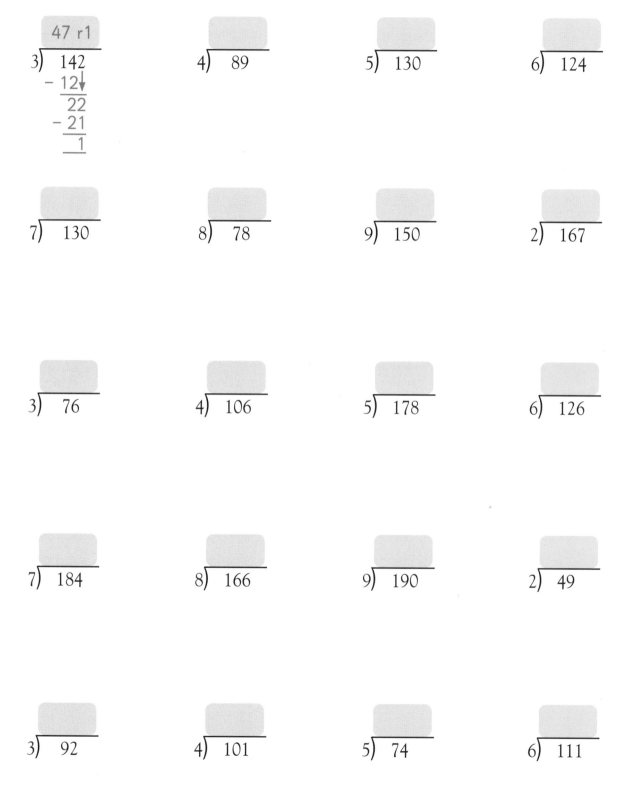

47 r1

3) 142
  − 12↓
    22
  − 21
     1

4) 89

5) 130

6) 124

7) 130

8) 78

9) 150

2) 167

3) 76

4) 106

5) 178

6) 126

7) 184

8) 166

9) 190

2) 49

3) 92

4) 101

5) 74

6) 111

Write the answers.

$$\begin{array}{r} 3.84 \\ +\ 1.39 \\ \hline \end{array}$$
5.23

$$\begin{array}{r} 4.29 \\ +\ 2.66 \\ \hline \end{array}$$

$$\begin{array}{r} 3.91 \\ +\ 4.22 \\ \hline \end{array}$$

$$\begin{array}{r} 5.16 \\ +\ 3.45 \\ \hline \end{array}$$

$$\begin{array}{r} 7.43 \\ +\ 2.66 \\ \hline \end{array}$$

$$\begin{array}{r} 2.33 \\ +\ 9.17 \\ \hline \end{array}$$

$$\begin{array}{r} 8.92 \\ +\ 3.17 \\ \hline \end{array}$$

$$\begin{array}{r} 5.26 \\ +\ 3.75 \\ \hline \end{array}$$

$$\begin{array}{r} 11.46 \\ +\ 6.56 \\ \hline \end{array}$$

$$\begin{array}{r} 19.32 \\ +\ 3.84 \\ \hline \end{array}$$

$$\begin{array}{r} 16.67 \\ +\ 4.21 \\ \hline \end{array}$$

$$\begin{array}{r} 18.74 \\ +\ 6.06 \\ \hline \end{array}$$

$$\begin{array}{r} 15.03 \\ +\ 18.78 \\ \hline \end{array}$$

$$\begin{array}{r} 14.92 \\ +\ 2.37 \\ \hline \end{array}$$

$$\begin{array}{r} 10.45 \\ +\ 5.93 \\ \hline \end{array}$$

$$\begin{array}{r} 12.67 \\ +\ 18.06 \\ \hline \end{array}$$

$$\begin{array}{r} 32.08 \\ +\ 7.92 \\ \hline \end{array}$$

$$\begin{array}{r} 46.02 \\ +\ 19.12 \\ \hline \end{array}$$

$$\begin{array}{r} 15.01 \\ +\ 14.99 \\ \hline \end{array}$$

$$\begin{array}{r} 17.84 \\ +\ 2.16 \\ \hline \end{array}$$

$$\begin{array}{r} 423.97 \\ +\ 67.94 \\ \hline \end{array}$$

$$\begin{array}{r} 301.75 \\ +\ 19.12 \\ \hline \end{array}$$

$$\begin{array}{r} 412.85 \\ +\ 56.73 \\ \hline \end{array}$$

$$\begin{array}{r} 213.52 \\ +\ 68.08 \\ \hline \end{array}$$

Write the answers.

4.78 − 1.44 **3.34**	9.52 − 4.56	8.74 − 3.11	3.97 − 1.84
7.82 − 3.49	6.13 − 2.08	3.27 − 1.45	5.24 − 4.01
9.04 − 2.53	6.01 − 2.67	8.06 − 3.57	4.79 − 1.32
16.05 − 11.45	12.42 − 8.67	18.67 − 12.37	10.23 − 3.78
413.65 − 213.65	215.07 − 180.01	312.56 − 121.65	569.72 − 236.09
500.05 − 1.06	150.06 − 100.09	200.01 − 99.99	420.69 − 89.43

Use the box for your working out.

 Dave delivers free magazines to houses and is paid 5 p per magazine. Dave delivers 600 magazines. How much will he earn?

Sean wins some money on four games at the fair. He wins 79 p, £1.38, £0.37 and 66 p. How much has Sean won in total?

Harris is a used car dealer and on a good day he sells three cars – a Honda for £7 850, a Ford for £5 999, and a Toyota for £8 499. What is the total value of the cars Harris sold that day?

 Emmie is given £20 for a Christmas present and spends £18.12 on clothes in the January sales. How much does Emmie have left?

A house in Middle Brook Street costs £285 000. The house next door is smaller and costs £228 000. What is the difference in the costs?

A large sack of potatoes costs £12.56. A smaller sack is half the price of the large sack. How much is the smaller sack?

Use the box for your working out.

Petrol costs £3.80 per litre. Donny's dad fills 20 litres of petrol in the car. How much will Donny's dad have to pay for the petrol?

The motorway route between Winchester and Cardiff is 127 miles. A route avoiding the motorway is 148.8 miles. How much shorter is the motorway route?

Rashid discovers that one-fifth of the strawberries in a pack are rotten. The pack contains 75 strawberries. How many strawberries are not rotten?

Mary measures the growth of a tomato plant. The plant grows 1.5 cm every week. How many weeks will it take for the plant to grow to 21 cm?

Nadia measures the distance she has to walk to school. She walks 875 m to school. How many metres will Nadia walk in five days?

A doctor sees one patient every seven minutes. How long will it take for the doctor to see 25 patients? (Answer in hours and minutes.)

These are the amounts collected at a church in one month.

£213.78   £197.56   £202.67   £184.26

What was the total amount collected in the month?

At the end of the year, each person owes £1 250 in taxes to the government.
Each person has the following amounts in their savings.

Sean has £12 600   Darius has £9 423   Emmie has £10 571

How much will each person have left after paying their taxes?

Sean   Darius   Emmie

Write the factors of each number.

32

64

Circle the numbers that are multiples of 12.   21   78

                                                              60

    50   90

24

110   120   20   132

These are times tables questions given to Jonas in a test. Jonas has written his answers.
Put a smiley face (☺) if Jonas has written the correct answer. If the answer is wrong,
then put a (✗).

6 x 8 = 48   3 x 12 =36   5 x 9 = 54   7 x 8 = 54

6 x 7 = 42   9 x 6 = 45   8 x 9 = 72   12 x 7 = 77

John thinks of a number and then multiplies it by 3.
He adds 6 to the new number and the result is 21.
What number did John start with?

What is the remainder in each division problem?

27 divided by 2

60 divided by 8

40 divided by 6

32 divided by 3

75 divided by 10

49 divided by 9

---

14 walkers each travel
1 250 km for a sponsored
walk. What is the total
distance the 14 walkers
have travelled?

Write the answers.

$$\begin{array}{r} 8.67 \\ + 4.88 \\ \hline \end{array}$$

$$\begin{array}{r} 12.45 \\ + 17.97 \\ \hline \end{array}$$

$$\begin{array}{r} 9.78 \\ + 12.06 \\ \hline \end{array}$$

A shopkeeper makes £1 312.86 in one day and
then pays his assistant £219.90 for the week's wages.
How much will the shopkeeper have left after he
pays his assistant?

Use the box for your working out.

A plane journey between London (Heathrow) and New York (JFK) takes 6 hours 35 minutes. If the plane leaves London at 9.35 a.m., at what time will it arrive at New York (London time)?

Sophie has to go shopping with her mother. They go shopping at 11.15 a.m. and return at 3.45 p.m. How long did the shopping take?

A railway station clock says the time is 3.07 p.m. The clock is 10 minutes fast. What is the actual time?

A bricklayer can lay 80 bricks in one hour. How many bricks will the bricklayer lay in eight hours?

Rashid takes 35 minutes to complete a quarter of his exercises. How long will it take Rashid to complete all his exercises? (Answer in hours and minutes.)

Lucy and Darius go on a boat trip around a lake. The trip lasts one and a half hours. If the trip begins at 2.45 p.m., at what time will it finish?

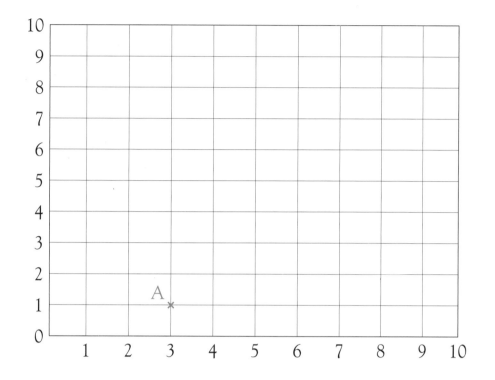

Mark the points A at (3,1) and B at (7,1).
Join A and B with a straight line.
What are the coordinates of the point
half way between A and B?

Mark the point C at (3,9).
Join A and C with a straight line.
What are the coordinates of the
half-way point between A and C?

Join the points C and B with a straight line.
What kind of triangle have you drawn?

....

Mark the points D at (5,7) and E at (7,7).
Join D and E with a straight line. What
are the coordinates of the half-way point
between D and E?

Mark the point F at (6,3).
Join F to D with a straight line.
Join F to E with a straight line.
What kind of triangle have you drawn?

....

Children from three classes were asked to vote for their favourite breakfast cereal.

Breakfast cereals	Frequency	Total
Maple Loops	卌 卌 卌 ‖	17
Weetynuts	卌 卌 卌 卌 卌 ⎮	
Corndunks	卌 卌 卌 卌 ‖‖‖	
Grainygrit	卌 ‖‖‖	
Coconutty	卌 卌 卌	

The frequency table shows the results. Look at the frequency table and then answer the questions. Complete the total column.

Which was the most popular breakfast cereal?   ....

What was the mean number of votes? (**Hint**: Mean means the average.)

What is the median amount of votes? (**Hint**: Median means the middle number.)

How many more votes did Weetynuts get than Maple Loops?

What was the range of the votes? (**Hint**: Range means the difference between the most and the least.)

What is the mode of each row? (**Hint**: Mode means the number used most.)

7   28   14   35   7   28   28   35

$\frac{1}{2}$ $\frac{1}{3}$ $\frac{1}{2}$ $\frac{1}{3}$ $\frac{1}{4}$ $\frac{1}{3}$ $\frac{1}{3}$ $\frac{1}{4}$

Perimeters ★

Calculate the perimeter of each shape.

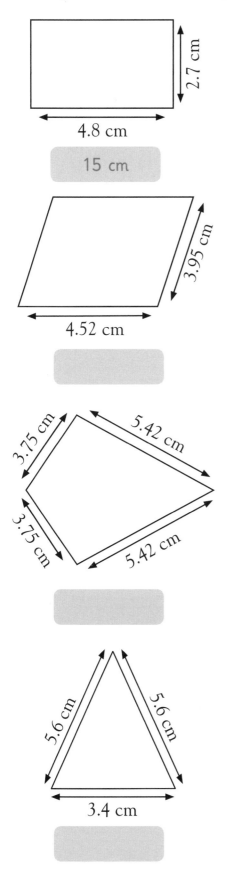

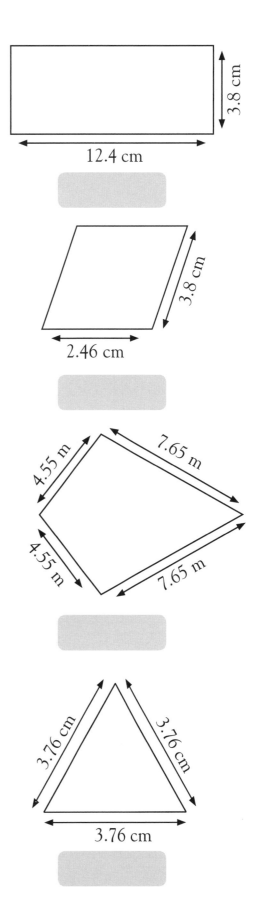

2.7 cm

4.8 cm

15 cm

3.8 cm

12.4 cm

3.95 cm

4.52 cm

3.8 cm

2.46 cm

3.75 cm   5.42 cm

3.75 cm   5.42 cm

4.55 m   7.65 m

4.55 m   7.65 m

5.6 cm   5.6 cm

3.4 cm

3.76 cm   3.76 cm

3.76 cm

Find the area of each shape.

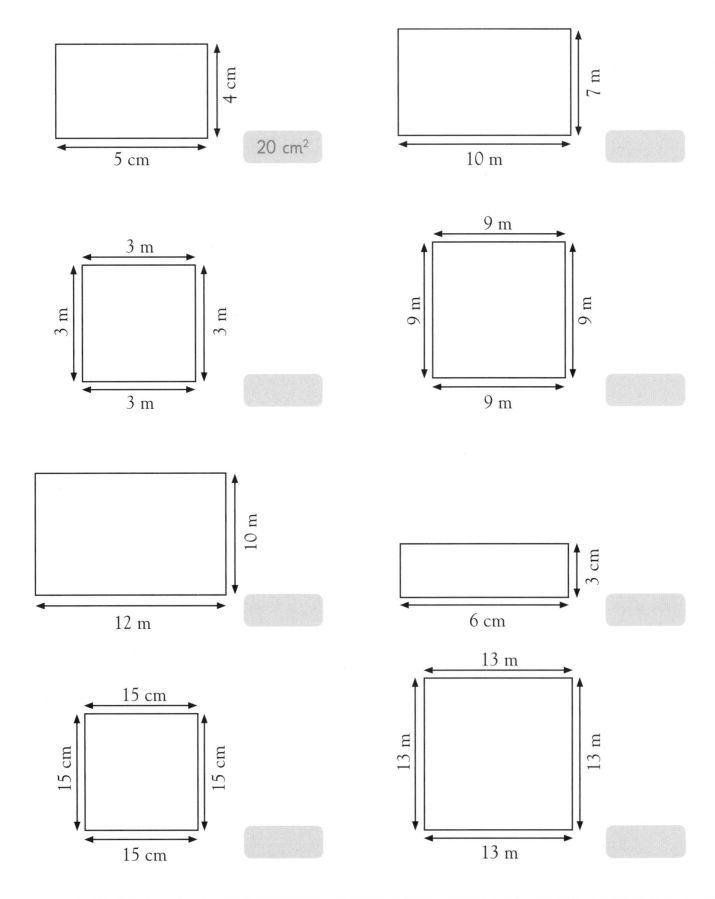

4 cm

5 cm

20 cm²

7 m

10 m

3 m

3 m

3 m

3 m

9 m

9 m

9 m

9 m

10 m

12 m

3 cm

6 cm

15 cm

15 cm

15 cm

15 cm

13 m

13 m

13 m

13 m

Use a protractor to measure each angle.

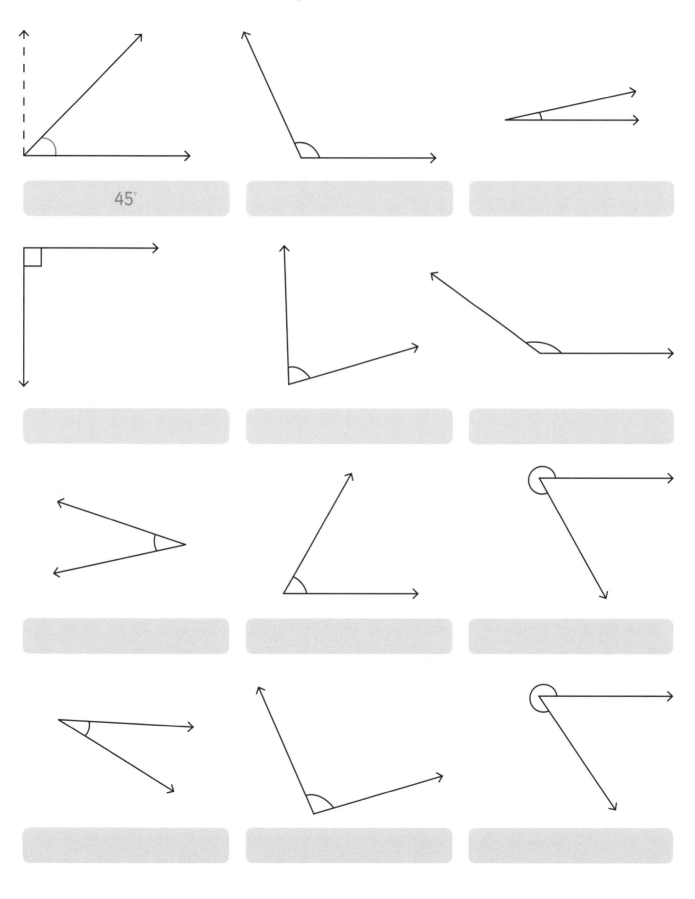

45°

These two clocks show times in the morning. What is the difference between them?

Look at the lengths of these pieces of wood.

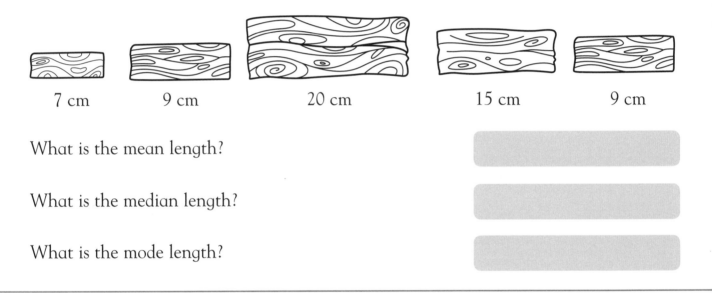

7 cm   9 cm   20 cm   15 cm   9 cm

What is the mean length?

What is the median length?

What is the mode length?

What is the perimeter of this school playground?

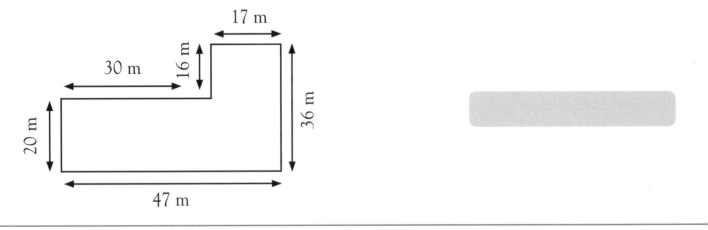

Circle the numbers that are not perfect squares.

16   20   40   60   36   49   100   88   4

Draw one of each type of angle. You do not need to use a protractor but make sure you mark the angle correctly.

| Right angle | Acute angle | Obtuse angle | Reflex angle |

Use a protractor to carefully measure each angle.

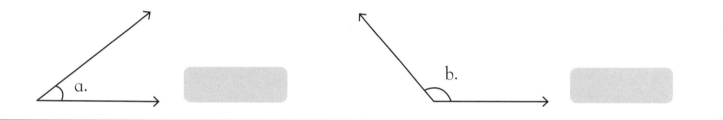

Use a protractor to carefully draw these angles.

67°

163°

Mark the points on this grid.

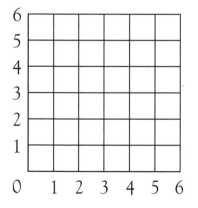

A = (3,5)   B = (5,0)

C = (4, $1\frac{1}{2}$)   D = (0, $5\frac{1}{2}$)

Certificate

Congratulations to

....

for successfully finishing this book.

Ages 9-10

WELL DONE!

You're a star.

☆ ☆ ☆ ☆ ☆

Date

....

Answer Section with Parents' Notes

This book helps to support children's understanding of mathematics as they become more proficient and fluent in applying and calculating maths.

Contents

By working through this book, your child will practise:

- understanding of place value of over 1 000 000;
- generating numerical sequences;
- solving multi-digit multiplication and division with remainders;
- using the four operations with decimal notation;
- recognising fraction equivalents to decimals and percentages;
- recognising factors and multiples;
- solving money and real-life problems;
- calculating perimeters and areas;
- representing and interpreting data;
- solving problems with units of measurement.

How to help your child

When checking the answers with your children, encourage them to explain their reasoning. This will emphasize the fact that you too recognise the value of maths and are able to understand how your child is thinking and where the stumbling blocks may be.

Around the home, continue to provide opportunities for practical use of measuring equipment and appropriate tools, such as calculators, scales, timetables, and computer programmes. This will help children to visualise situations when answering maths problems.

Build your children's confidence with words of praise. If they are getting answers wrong, then encourage them to return to try again another time. Good luck and remember to have fun.

★ Place value

Write each of these in numbers.

Fifteen thousand, seven hundred and twenty nine	15 729
Six hundred and eighteen thousand, two hundred and forty three	618 243
Five million, six hundred thousand and four	5 600 004
One hundred and seven thousand, two hundred and fifty six	107 256
Three hundred thousand, two hundred and eighteen	300 218
Eight hundred and six thousand, one hundred and seven	806 107
Three hundred and twenty-one thousand, five hundred and fifty nine	321 559
Nine hundred and ninety-nine thousand, nine hundred and ninety nine	999 999
Two million, three hundred and forty-seven thousand, one hundred and sixty nine	2 347 169
Eight million, two hundred and five thousand, four hundred and one	8 205 401

Write each row in order, starting with the smallest number.

721 358	8 213 560	6 234 078	1 200 000
721 358	1 200 000	6 234 078	8 213 560

9 999 999	999 999	10 000 000	9 000 009
999 999	9 000 009	9 999 999	10 000 000

Write each number in words.

2 301 502 Two million, three hundred and one thousand, five hundred and two

7 582 416 Seven million, five hundred and eighty-two thousand, four hundred and sixteen

Children will seldom encounter very large numbers and so need practice to understand how they are shown. Sometimes, children can be confused when a 0 is a placeholder as with 12 045 for example.

Multiply and divide by 10 and 100 ★

Write the answers.

269 x 10 =	2 690	7 650 ÷ 10 =	765
845 x 10 =	8 450	52 430 ÷ 10 =	5 243
1 564 x 10 =	15 640	76 400 ÷ 10 =	7 640
7 405 x 10 =	74 050	600 000 ÷ 10 =	60 000
7 420 x 10 =	74 200	1 435 290 ÷ 10 =	143 529
15 645 x 10 =	156 450	1 350 000 ÷ 10 =	135 000
23 785 x 10 =	237 850	5 500 430 ÷ 10 =	550 043
54 866 x 10 =	548 660	8 412 600 ÷ 10 =	841 260
299 400 x 10 =	2 994 000	10 000 000 ÷ 10 =	1 000 000
324 545 x 10 =	3 245 450	376 800 ÷ 100 =	3 768
465 212 x 10 =	4 652 120	656 000 ÷ 100 =	6 560
2 867 x 100 =	286 700	1 345 000 ÷ 100 =	13 450
26 734 x 100 =	2 673 400	5 000 000 ÷ 100 =	50 000
65 089 x 100 =	6 508 900	5 560 200 ÷ 100 =	55 602
72 967 x 100 =	7 296 700	8 400 000 ÷ 100 =	84 000
300 000 x 100 =	30 000 000	8 006 000 ÷ 100 =	80 060

Although it is simple to tell children to "add a 0 when multiplying by 10" or something similar for multiplying by 100 or dividing by 10 and 100, it is important they understand the principle that each number becomes 10 or 100 times larger or smaller.

★ Ordering sets of amounts

Write each row in order, starting with the smallest number.

7 m	690 cm	1.6 km	900 m	1 700 m
690 cm	7 m	900 m	1.6 km	1 700 m

23 cm	240 mm	180 mm	20 cm	0.21 m
180 mm	20 cm	0.21 m	23 cm	240 mm

2.8 km	3 000 m	2.5 km	2 600 m	1.9 km
1.9 km	2.5 km	2 600 m	2.8 km	3 000 m

678 g	0.5 kg	2.3 kg	1 400 g	0.95 kg
0.5 kg	678 g	0.95 kg	1 400 g	2.3 kg

1 200 ml	1.6 l	0.9 l	850 ml	1 400 ml
850 ml	0.9 l	1 200 ml	1 400 ml	1.6 l

£5.50	280 p	£0.75	600 p	£3.90
£0.75	280 p	£3.90	£5.50	600 p

12 l	11 000 ml	8.5 l	110.45 ml	6.85 l
110.45 ml	6.85 l	8.5 l	11 000 ml	12 l

150 seconds	3 minutes	1 hour	130 minutes	600 seconds
150 seconds	3 minutes	600 seconds	1 hour	130 minutes

$\frac{1}{2}$ l	$\frac{3}{5}$ l	1.2 l	0.25 l	2 l
0.25 l	$\frac{1}{2}$ l	$\frac{3}{5}$ l	1.2 l	2 l

2 hours	50 minutes	$3\frac{1}{2}$ hours	100 minutes	$1\frac{1}{2}$ hours
50 minutes	$1\frac{1}{2}$ hours	100 minutes	2 hours	$3\frac{1}{2}$ hours

Within each row, the units have been mixed up, so effectively these questions are not just about ordering by size but also encourage children to convert between units, as well as between decimal and fractional amounts.

Constant steps ★

Continue each sequence.

1.6	2.2	2.8	3.4	4.0	4.6	5.2	5.8
3.7	4.2	4.7	5.2	5.7	6.2	6.7	7.2
$1\frac{1}{2}$	$4\frac{1}{2}$	$7\frac{1}{2}$	$10\frac{1}{2}$	$13\frac{1}{2}$	$16\frac{1}{2}$	$19\frac{1}{2}$	$22\frac{1}{2}$
35	28	21	14	7	0	−7	−14
5.9	4.9	3.9	2.9	1.9	0.9	−0.1	−1.1
$6\frac{1}{4}$	$5\frac{3}{4}$	$5\frac{1}{4}$	$4\frac{3}{4}$	$4\frac{1}{4}$	$3\frac{3}{4}$	$3\frac{1}{4}$	$2\frac{3}{4}$
−6.5	−5.6	−4.7	−3.8	−2.9	−2.0	−1.1	−0.2
34	45	56	67	78	89	100	111
8.6	9.2	9.8	10.4	11.0	11.6	12.2	12.8
30	45	60	75	90	105	120	135
−50	−44	−38	−32	−26	−20	−14	−8
0.6	1.1	1.6	2.1	2.6	3.1	3.6	4.1
4.6	7.6	10.6	13.6	16.6	19.6	22.6	25.6
14.4	13.9	13.4	12.9	12.4	11.9	11.4	10.9
7.3	6.3	5.3	4.3	3.3	2.3	1.3	0.3

Children should do well with these questions as long as they spot how the numbers are changing and then correctly calculate the next in the sequence. The sequences that go from positive to negative numbers can be trickier.

★ Calculating temperatures

Use the thermometer to count the number of degrees from one temperature to another to answer these questions.

What is the difference in temperatures?

5°C and 12°C	7°C	10°C and 3°C	7°C
1°C and 14°C	13°C	4°C and 0°C	4°C
8°C and 20°C	12°C	18°C and 30°C	12°C
15°C and 25°C	10°C	10°C and 14°C	4°C
19°C and 12°C	7°C	5°C and -2°C	7°C
-3°C and 7°C	10°C	8°C and -1°C	9°C
-4°C and 4°C	8°C	9°C and 0°C	9°C
6°C and -3°C	9°C	-8°C and 3°C	11°C
10°C and -3°C	13°C	-5°C and 12°C	17°C
-3°C and -4°C	1°C	-6°C and -8°C	2°C
0°C and -5°C	5°C	0°C and -20°C	20°C
-10°C and -30°C	20°C	-4°C and -12°C	8°C

Thermometer readings: 30, 20, 10, 0, -10, -20, -30 °C

The temperature in London, U.K. is 5°C but the temperature in Moscow, Russia is 8°C colder. What is the temperature in Moscow? — -3°C

The temperature in Madrid, Spain is 12°C warmer than the temperature in Toronto, Canada. The temperature in Toronto is -3°C. What is the temperature in Madrid? — 9°C

The temperature in Paris, France is 7°C and in Helsinki, Finland is -4°C. What is the difference in temperature between Paris and Helsinki? — 11°C

If children have any doubt regarding this type of work, encourage them to draw a simple number line going from a positive value, such as 20, to a negative number such as −20. Let them make marks on the line or just point to numbers.

Fractions of amounts ★

What is one-quarter ($\frac{1}{4}$) of each amount?

12 p — 3 p	40 p — 10 p	60 p — 15 p	£1.00 — 25 p	£8.00 — £2
24 cm — 6 cm	36 cm — 9 cm	4 m — 1 m	16 cm — 4 cm	240 cm — 60 cm
8 kg — 2 kg	28 g — 7 g	44 kg — 11 kg	52 kg — 13 kg	120 g — 30 g

What is two-thirds ($\frac{2}{3}$) of each amount?

21 km — 14 km	27 kg — 18 kg	15 p — 10 p	£30 — £20	18 cm — 12 cm
12 l — 8 l	9 cm — 6 cm	30 m — 20 m	45 kg — 30 kg	60 mm — 40 mm
24 ml — 16 ml	36 m — 24 m	90 km — 60 km	48 cm — 32 cm	£120 — £80

What is three-quarters ($\frac{3}{4}$) of each amount?

£1.00 — 75 p	£1.60 — £1.20	£1.12 — 84 p	£1.40 — £1.05	£10.00 — £7.50
96 p — 72 p	84 p — 63 p	72 p — 54 p	56 p — 42 p	104 p — 78 p
240 m — 180 m	400 m — 300 m	600 m — 450 m	480 m — 360 m	220 m — 165 m

What is four-fifths ($\frac{4}{5}$) of each amount?

350 g — 280 g	8 m — 6.4 m	£5 — £4	15 km — 12 km	20 m — 16 m
100 mm — 80 mm	80 m — 64 m	60 p — 48 p	90 cm — 72 cm	30 p — 24 p
500 km — 400 km	£2 — £1.60	250 p — 200 p	£120 — £96	900 m — 720 m

By this stage, children can calculate unitary fractions ($\frac{1}{2}$, $\frac{1}{3}$, $\frac{1}{4}$) as long as their knowledge of times tables is good. For other fractions ($\frac{2}{3}$, $\frac{3}{4}$, $\frac{4}{5}$), the simplest method is to work out one part and then multiply by whatever is needed.

★ Fractions to decimals

Write each fraction in its decimal form.

$\frac{1}{2}$ — 0.5	$\frac{1}{4}$ — 0.25	$\frac{3}{4}$ — 0.75	$\frac{1}{5}$ — 0.2	$\frac{2}{5}$ — 0.4
$\frac{3}{5}$ — 0.6	$\frac{4}{5}$ — 0.8	$\frac{1}{3}$ — 0.3̄3	$\frac{2}{3}$ — 0.6̄6	$\frac{1}{10}$ — 0.1
$\frac{2}{10}$ — 0.2	$\frac{3}{10}$ — 0.3	$\frac{5}{10}$ — 0.5	$\frac{6}{10}$ — 0.6	$\frac{9}{10}$ — 0.9

Write each number in its decimal form.

$1\frac{1}{2}$ — 1.5	$7\frac{1}{2}$ — 7.5	$4\frac{1}{3}$ — 4.3̄3	$7\frac{2}{3}$ — 7.6̄6	$9\frac{1}{4}$ — 9.25
$6\frac{1}{5}$ — 6.2	$9\frac{3}{10}$ — 9.3	$2\frac{9}{10}$ — 2.9	$12\frac{1}{3}$ — 12.3̄3	$15\frac{2}{3}$ — 15.6̄6
$8\frac{4}{5}$ — 8.8	$5\frac{3}{4}$ — 5.75	$7\frac{8}{10}$ — 7.8	$15\frac{3}{5}$ — 15.6	$2\frac{4}{10}$ — 2.4
$14\frac{2}{3}$ — 14.6̄6	$18\frac{3}{4}$ — 18.75	$12\frac{3}{4}$ — 12.75	$2\frac{1}{2}$ — 2.5	$15\frac{6}{10}$ — 15.6

Join the shaded fraction to its decimal form with a line.

$\frac{3}{10}$ ——— 0.4
$\frac{4}{5}$ ——— 0.75
$\frac{9}{10}$ ——— 0.2
$\frac{1}{5}$ ——— 0.3
$\frac{3}{4}$ ——— 0.9
$\frac{2}{5}$ ——— 0.8

Children should know the simpler conversions by now. Although $\frac{1}{3}$ is shown as 0.3̄3 and $\frac{2}{3}$ as 0.6̄6, the mark above the hundredths number indicates that the decimal actually continues to infinity and is known as "repeating".

Percentages ★

Change each fraction to its percentage equivalent.

$\frac{1}{2}$ = 50%	$\frac{1}{4}$ = 25%	$\frac{3}{4}$ = 75%	$\frac{1}{5}$ = 20%
$\frac{2}{5}$ = 40%	$\frac{3}{5}$ = 60%	$\frac{4}{5}$ = 80%	$\frac{1}{10}$ = 10%
$\frac{2}{10}$ = 20%	$\frac{3}{10}$ = 30%	$\frac{4}{10}$ = 40%	$\frac{5}{10}$ = 50%
$\frac{6}{10}$ = 60%	$\frac{7}{10}$ = 70%	$\frac{8}{10}$ = 80%	$\frac{9}{10}$ = 90%
$\frac{50}{100}$ = 50%	$\frac{80}{100}$ = 80%	$\frac{10}{100}$ = 10%	$\frac{20}{100}$ = 20%
$\frac{90}{100}$ = 90%	$\frac{40}{100}$ = 40%	$\frac{70}{100}$ = 70%	$\frac{30}{100}$ = 30%
$\frac{60}{100}$ = 60%	$\frac{25}{100}$ = 25%	$\frac{75}{100}$ = 75%	$\frac{5}{100}$ = 5%
$\frac{17}{100}$ = 17%	$\frac{28}{100}$ = 28%	$\frac{35}{100}$ = 35%	$\frac{46}{100}$ = 46%
$\frac{52}{100}$ = 52%	$\frac{63}{100}$ = 63%	$\frac{76}{100}$ = 76%	$\frac{83}{100}$ = 83%

Write each amount as a percentage of one pound (£).

27 p — 27%	35 p — 35%	60 p — 60%	90 p — 90%
41 p — 41%	12 p — 12%	42 p — 42%	79 p — 79%
75 p — 75%	56 p — 56%	30 p — 30%	80 p — 80%

What is 20% of each amount? **Hint:** 20% = $\frac{20}{100}$ or $\frac{1}{5}$.

£2.00 — 40 p	£5.00 — £1	10 km — 2 km	400 m — 80 m

As with conversions between fraction and decimal amounts, children should become used to percentages as another way of showing proportional amounts. It is useful if your child learns that 1 pence is 1% of a pound and so on.

★ Keeping skills sharp

Ten people win a lottery prize of £1 345 279. The prize is shared equally between them. How much will they each receive? | £134 527.90

A scientist has to put some animals on display in order of their length. The smallest animal must go first. Below are the lengths of some animals. Put these lengths in order, starting with the shortest.

27 m	3 750 cm	18.25 m	99 mm	0.87 m
99 mm	0.87 m	18.25 m	27 m	3 750 cm

A child reduces each of these amounts by 8 units every minute. What will the amounts be after 5 minutes?

	After 1 min	After 2 min	After 3 min	After 4 min	After 5 min
62 g	54 g	46 g	38 g	30 g	22 g
79 cm	71 cm	63 cm	55 cm	47 cm	39 cm
102 ml	94 ml	86 ml	78 ml	70 ml	62 ml

The temperature in a freezer drops steadily by 2 °C per hour. If the freezer starts at –1 °C, what will the temperature be after six hours? | –13 °C

Put each row in order, starting with the smallest number.

7.5	5.7	7.05	5.07	5.55	5.75
5.07	5.55	5.7	5.75	7.05	7.5
12.8	1.28	0.12	0.28	2.18	1.82
0.12	0.28	1.28	1.82	2.18	12.8
34.06	30.46	36.4	36.04	30.64	34.6
30.46	30.64	34.06	34.6	36.04	36.4

The 10 questions on this page and the following are intended to act as a small test of the preceding work. It is up to you to decide if a time limit should be set but something like 10 minutes would be about right.

Keeping skills sharp ★

Circle the fractions that are equivalent to $\frac{3}{4}$.

$\frac{30}{40}$ $\frac{9}{10}$ $\frac{4}{6}$ $\frac{12}{16}$ $\frac{300}{400}$ $\frac{18}{30}$

Boris has five children. Each child has a certain amount of money.

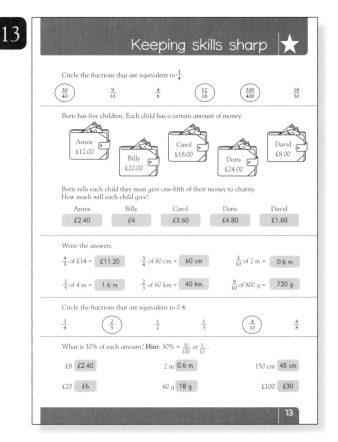

Annie £12.00   Billy £20.00   Carol £18.00   Doris £24.00   David £8.00

Boris tells each child they must give one-fifth of their money to charity. How much will each child give?

Annie	Billy	Carol	Doris	David
£2.40	£4	£3.60	£4.80	£1.60

Write the answers.

$\frac{4}{5}$ of £14 = £11.20 $\frac{3}{4}$ of 80 cm = 60 cm $\frac{3}{10}$ of 2 m = 0.6 m

$\frac{2}{5}$ of 4 m = 1.6 m $\frac{2}{3}$ of 60 km = 40 km $\frac{9}{10}$ of 800 g = 720 g

Circle the fractions that are equivalent to 0.4.

$\frac{3}{4}$ $\frac{2}{5}$ $\frac{1}{2}$ $\frac{1}{3}$ $\frac{4}{10}$ $\frac{4}{8}$

What is 30% of each amount? **Hint:** 30% = $\frac{30}{100}$ or $\frac{3}{10}$.

£8 £2.40   2 m 0.6 m   150 cm 45 cm

£20 £6   60 g 18 g   £100 £30

Clearly, it would be important to go over any questions that may be wrong, but give plenty of encouragement for those that are correct.

★ Recognising multiples

Circle the multiples of 12.

50   (24)   (60)   (144)
38   70   80   100   90
(36)   (120)   56   94

Circle the multiples of 15.

(45)   10   (60)   130
80   70   (75)   100   (90)
1   (150)   50   65

Circle the multiples of 20.

15   (20)   310   110
(60)   90   70   (100)   (400)
(500)   130   (200)   30

Circle the multiples of 50.

(50)   20   (350)   (500)
(750)   (1 000)   70   (100)   (400)
(300)   130   240   470

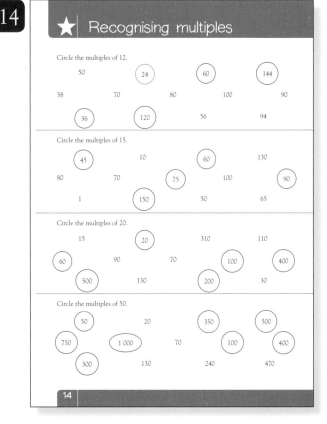

Children should understand what the word "multiple" means and be able to work out some of the more usual ones such as 12 or 20.

Factors of numbers ★

Write the factors of these numbers. Always begin with 1.
Remember: If a number is even, 2 will always be a factor.

The factors of 10 are | 1, 2, 5, 10

The factors of 12 are | 1, 2, 3, 4, 6, 12

The factors of 18 are | 1, 2, 3, 6, 9, 18

The factors of 51 are | 1, 3, 17, 51

The factors of 61 are | 1, 61

The factors of 71 are | 1, 71

The factors of 81 are | 1, 3, 9, 27, 81

The factors of 60 are | 1, 2, 3, 4, 5, 6, 10, 12, 15, 20, 30, 60

The factors of 70 are | 1, 2, 5, 7, 10, 14, 35, 70

The factors of 75 are | 1, 3, 5, 15, 25, 75

The factors of 85 are | 1, 5, 17, 85

The factors of 29 are | 1, 29

The factors of 53 are | 1, 53

The factors of 24 are | 1, 2, 3, 4, 6, 8, 12, 24

Factors of larger numbers can be difficult to spot. Encourage children to work through the possibilities logically. Be careful they don't assume numbers are not factors because the numbers are large, for example 3 is a factor of 51.

★ Multiplying in columns

Work out these multiplication sums, using the method you prefer.

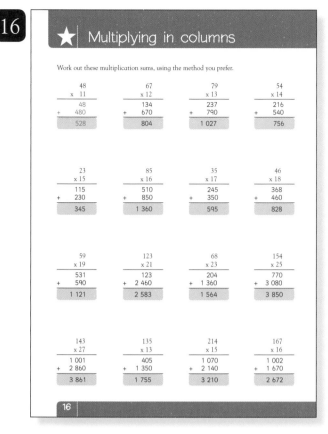

The questions on this page have been laid out in the traditional column style. If your child has been taught another method, check to see how it works. Avoid changing the method the school has taught as this could cause confusion.

Dividing with remainders ★

You may have been shown different ways to work out these problems. Use the method you prefer to find the quotient and remainders.

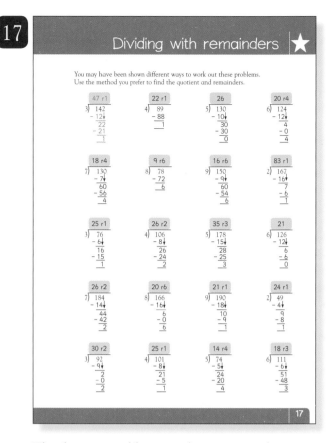

The division problems on this page are shown in the traditional format but parents should be aware, as with multiplication, that schools may teach other methods. Success with this work depends greatly on good times-tables knowledge.

★ Adding decimals

Write the answers.

3.84 + 1.39 = **5.23**	4.29 + 2.66 = **6.95**	3.91 + 4.22 = **8.13**	5.16 + 3.45 = **8.61**
7.43 + 2.66 = **10.09**	2.33 + 9.17 = **11.50**	8.92 + 3.17 = **12.09**	5.26 + 3.75 = **9.01**
11.46 + 6.56 = **18.02**	19.32 + 3.84 = **23.16**	16.67 + 4.21 = **20.88**	18.74 + 6.06 = **24.80**
15.03 + 18.78 = **33.81**	14.92 + 2.37 = **17.29**	10.45 + 5.93 = **16.38**	12.67 + 18.06 = **30.73**
32.08 + 7.92 = **40.00**	46.02 + 19.12 = **65.14**	15.01 + 14.99 = **30.00**	17.84 + 2.16 = **20.00**
423.97 + 67.94 = **491.91**	301.75 + 19.12 = **320.87**	412.85 + 56.73 = **469.58**	213.52 + 68.08 = **281.60**

Children need to add each column carefully and then "carry" if necessary. Remind them to place the decimal point in the correct place as some children forget to put it in the answer.

Subtracting decimals ★

Write the answers.

4.78 − 1.44 = **3.34**	9.52 − 4.56 = **4.96**	8.74 − 3.11 = **5.63**	3.97 − 1.84 = **2.13**
7.82 − 3.49 = **4.33**	6.13 − 2.08 = **4.05**	3.27 − 1.45 = **1.82**	5.24 − 4.01 = **1.23**
9.04 − 2.53 = **6.51**	6.01 − 2.67 = **3.34**	8.06 − 3.57 = **4.49**	4.79 − 1.32 = **3.47**
16.05 − 11.45 = **4.60**	12.42 − 8.67 = **3.75**	18.67 − 12.37 = **6.30**	10.23 − 3.78 = **6.45**
413.65 − 213.65 = **200.00**	215.07 − 180.01 = **35.06**	312.56 − 121.65 = **190.91**	569.72 − 236.09 = **333.63**
500.05 − 1.06 = **498.99**	150.06 − 100.09 = **49.97**	200.01 − 99.99 = **100.02**	420.69 − 89.43 = **331.26**

Children need to be careful with each calculation, especially when it becomes necessary to "steal" from the next column. The phrase "borrow" is incorrect because the amount is never given back. The school may teach a different method.

★ Money problems

Use the box for your working out.

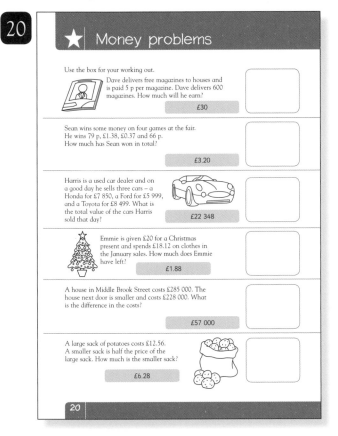

Dave delivers free magazines to houses and is paid 5 p per magazine. Dave delivers 600 magazines. How much will he earn?

£30

Sean wins some money on four games at the fair. He wins 79 p, £1.38, £0.37 and 66 p. How much has Sean won in total?

£3.20

Harris is a used car dealer and on a good day he sells three cars – a Honda for £7 850, a Ford for £5 999, and a Toyota for £8 499. What is the total value of the cars Harris sold that day?

£22 348

Emmie is given £20 for a Christmas present and spends £18.12 on clothes in the January sales. How much does Emmie have left?

£1.88

A house in Middle Brook Street costs £285 000. The house next door is smaller and costs £228 000. What is the difference in the costs?

£57 000

A large sack of potatoes costs £12.56. A smaller sack is half the price of the large sack. How much is the smaller sack?

£6.28

The main objective here is for children to select the right operation and then work the calculation carefully, quickly, and correctly.

Real-life problems ★

Use the box for your working out.

Petrol costs £3.80 per litre. Donny's dad fills 20 litres of petrol in the car. How much will Donny's dad have to pay for the petrol?

£76.00

The motorway route between Winchester and Cardiff is 127 miles. A route avoiding the motorway is 148.8 miles. How much shorter is the motorway route?

21.8 miles

Rashid discovers that one-fifth of the strawberries in a pack are rotten. The pack contains 75 strawberries. How many strawberries are not rotten?

60 strawberries

Mary measures the growth of a tomato plant. The plant grows 1.5 cm every week. How many weeks will it take for the plant to grow to 21 cm?

14 weeks

Nadia measures the distance she has to walk to school. She walks 875 m to school. How many metres will Nadia walk in five days?

4 375 metres

A doctor sees one patient every seven minutes. How long will it take for the doctor to see 25 patients? (Answer in hours and minutes.)

2 hours 55 minutes

Putting the four operations into practical use is most important and something schools don't always do so. Children need to work out which is the right operation to use to produce the correct answer.

★ Keeping skills sharp

These are the amounts collected at a church in one month.

£213.78   £197.56   £202.67   £184.26

What was the total amount collected in the month?   £798.27

At the end of the year, each person owes £1 250 in taxes to the government. Each person has the following amounts in their savings.

Sean has £12 600   Darius has £9 423   Emmie has £10 571

How much will each person have left after paying their taxes?

Sean   £11 350   Darius   £8 173   Emmie   £9 321

Write the factors of each number.

32   1, 2, 4, 8, 16, 32

64   1, 2, 4, 8, 16, 32, 64

Circle the numbers that are multiples of 12.

21   78

(24)   50   (60)

110   90   (120)   (132)

20

These are times tables questions given to Jonas in a test. Jonas has written his answers. Put a smiley face (☺) if Jonas has written the correct answer. If the answer is wrong, then put a (✗).

6 x 8 = 48 ☺   3 x 12 = 36 ☺   5 x 9 = 54 ✗   7 x 8 = 54 ✗

6 x 7 = 42 ☺   9 x 6 = 45 ✗   8 x 9 = 72 ☺   12 x 7 = 77 ✗

This test covers the work undertaken in the previous pages and will act as a reminder and as a way of judging how well learning has taken place.

Keeping skills sharp ★

John thinks of a number and then multiplies it by 3. He adds 6 to the new number and the result is 21. What number did John start with?   5

What is the remainder in each division problem?

27 divided by 2   1   32 divided by 3   2

60 divided by 8   4   75 divided by 10   5

40 divided by 6   4   49 divided by 9   4

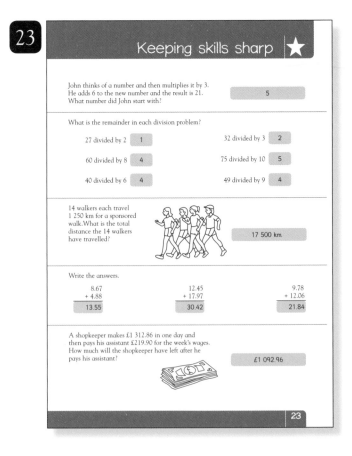

14 walkers each travel 1 250 km for a sponsored walk. What is the total distance the 14 walkers have travelled?   17 500 km

Write the answers.

8.67	12.45	9.78
+ 4.88	+ 17.97	+ 12.06
13.55	30.42	21.84

A shopkeeper makes £1 312.86 in one day and then pays his assistant £219.90 for the week's wages. How much will the shopkeeper have left after he pays his assistant?   £1 092.96

★ Time problems

Use the box for your working out.

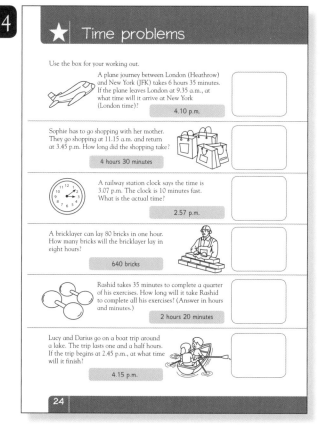

A plane journey between London (Heathrow) and New York (JFK) takes 6 hours 35 minutes. If the plane leaves London at 9.35 a.m., at what time will it arrive at New York (London time)?

4.10 p.m.

Sophie has to go shopping with her mother. They go shopping at 11.15 a.m. and return at 3.45 p.m. How long did the shopping take?

4 hours 30 minutes

A railway station clock says the time is 3.07 p.m. The clock is 10 minutes fast. What is the actual time?

2.57 p.m.

A bricklayer can lay 80 bricks in one hour. How many bricks will the bricklayer lay in eight hours?

640 bricks

Rashid takes 35 minutes to complete a quarter of his exercises. How long will it take Rashid to complete all his exercises? (Answer in hours and minutes.)

2 hours 20 minutes

Lucy and Darius go on a boat trip around a lake. The trip lasts one and a half hours. If the trip begins at 2.45 p.m., at what time will it finish?

4.15 p.m.

By this age, children should be very familiar with analogue and digital time displays and be able to change between them. Have a clock or watch nearby to demonstrate any problem if necessary.

Coordinates ★

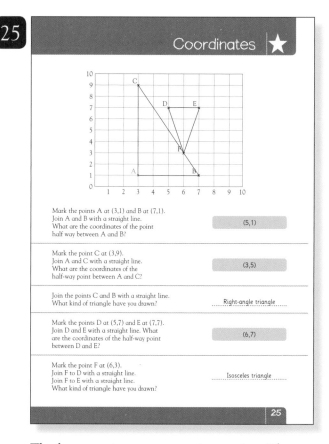

Mark the points A at (3,1) and B at (7,1). Join A and B with a straight line. What are the coordinates of the point half way between A and B?

(5,1)

Mark the point C at (3,9). Join A and C with a straight line. What are the coordinates of the half-way point between A and C?

(3,5)

Join the points C and B with a straight line. What kind of triangle have you drawn?

Right-angle triangle

Mark the points D at (5,7) and E at (7,7). Join D and E with a straight line. What are the coordinates of the half-way point between D and E?

(6,7)

Mark the point F at (6,3). Join F to D with a straight line. Join F to E with a straight line. What kind of triangle have you drawn?

Isosceles triangle

The last question may prove interesting. The isosceles triangle is "upside down" compared to the one children usually see. It may be interesting if they fail to recognise it without the page being turned upside down.

★ Using data

Children from three classes were asked to vote for their favourite breakfast cereal.

Breakfast cereals	Frequency	Total
Maple Loops	ЖЖЖ II	17
Weetynuts	ЖЖЖЖЖ I	26
Corndunks	ЖЖЖЖ IIII	24
Grainygrit	Ж III	8
Coconutty	ЖЖЖ	15

The frequency table shows the results. Look at the frequency table and then answer the questions. Complete the total column.

Which was the most popular breakfast cereal? — Weetynuts

What was the mean number of votes? (**Hint:** Mean means the average.) — 18

What is the median amount of votes? (**Hint:** Median means the middle number.) — 17

How many more votes did Weetynuts get than Maple Loops? — 9

What was the range of the votes? (**Hint:** Range means the difference between the most and the least.) — 18

What is the mode of each row? (**Hint:** Mode means the number used most.)

7   28   14   35   7   28   28   35 — 28

$\frac{1}{2}$ $\frac{1}{3}$ $\frac{1}{2}$ $\frac{1}{3}$ $\frac{1}{4}$ $\frac{1}{3}$ $\frac{1}{3}$ $\frac{1}{4}$ — $\frac{1}{3}$

In simple terms, mode is the number that occurs most often and median is the middle number when the numbers are arranged in order. The range is the difference between the lowest and highest values.

Perimeters ★

Calculate the perimeter of each shape.

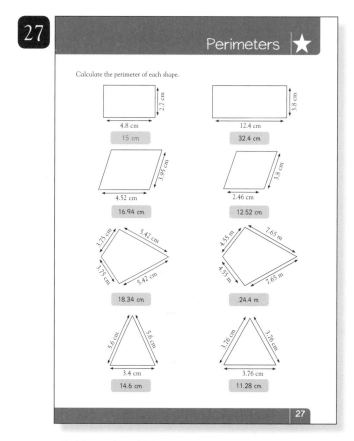

4.8 cm, 2.7 cm — 15 cm

12.4 cm, 3.8 cm — 32.4 cm

4.52 cm, 3.95 cm — 16.94 cm

2.46 cm, 3.8 cm — 12.52 cm

3.75 cm, 5.42 cm, 3.75 cm, 5.42 cm — 18.34 cm

4.55 m, 7.65 m, 4.55 m, 7.65 m — 24.4 m

5.6 cm, 5.6 cm, 3.4 cm — 14.6 cm

3.76 cm, 3.76 cm, 3.76 cm — 11.28 cm

Children should know "perimeter" means the distance around the outside of a shape. With these perimeters, they need to be careful about adding the decimal amounts.

★ Areas

Find the area of each shape.

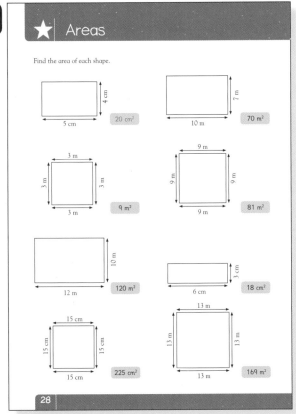

20 cm²

70 m²

9 m²

81 m²

120 m²

18 cm²

225 cm²

169 m²

The answers can be written as "square metre" or "metres squared" but are usually written in the m² style.

Measuring angles ★

Use a protractor to measure each angle.

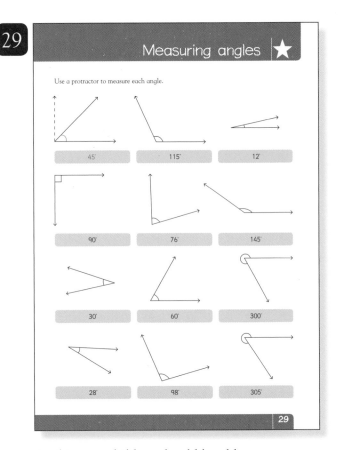

45°

115°

12°

90°

76°

145°

30°

60°

300°

28°

98°

305°

At this age, children should be able to measure each angle exactly. For the larger angles such as 300°, it is best to measure the smaller angle and then subtract that from 360°. This technique will not be needed with circular protractors.

★ Keeping skills sharp

These two clocks show times in the morning. What is the difference between them?

3:25

5 hours and 45 minutes

Look at the lengths of these pieces of wood.

7 cm   9 cm   20 cm   15 cm   9 cm

What is the mean length?   12 cm

What is the median length?   9 cm

What is the mode length?   9 cm

What is the perimeter of this school playground?

17 m
30 m
16 m
36 m
20 m
47 m

166 m

Circle the numbers that are not perfect squares.

16   (20)   (40)   (60)   36   49   100   (88)   4

The final test covers the work of the previous pages. Encourage children to seek advice if an answer is wrong and then go through it very carefully until they gain confidence.

Keeping skills sharp ★

Draw one of each type of angle. You do not need to use a protractor but make sure you mark the angle correctly. Answers may vary.

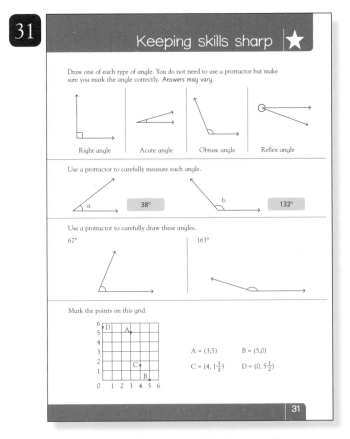

Right angle   Acute angle   Obtuse angle   Reflex angle

Use a protractor to carefully measure each angle.

a.   38°

b.   132°

Use a protractor to carefully draw these angles.

67°   163°

Mark the points on this grid.

A = (3,5)   B = (5,0)

C = (4, 1½)   D = (0, 5½)

The *Maths Made Easy* workbooks provide more practice pages.